# PLANTS vs. ZOMBIES

## TIMEPOCALYPSE

Written by **PAUL TOBIN**
Art by **RON CHAN**
Colors by **MATTHEW J. RAINWATER**
Letters by **STEVE DUTRO**
Cover by **RON CHAN**

DARK HORSE BOOKS

# PLANTS VS. ZOMBIES

## TIMEPOCALYPSE

Publisher **MIKE RICHARDSON**
Editor **PHILIP R. SIMON**
Assistant Editor **ROXY POLK**
Designer **KAT LARSON**
Digital Production **CHRISTINA McKENZIE**

Special thanks to **LEIGH BEACH, SHANA DOERR,
A.J. RATHBUN, BRENNAN TOWNLEY, JEREMY
VANHOOZER,** and everyone at PopCap Games.

Scholastic edition: January 2015
ISBN 978-1-61655-832-1

10 9 8 7 6 5 4 3 2 1
Printed in China

**DarkHorse.com | PopCap.com**

▷ No plants were harmed in the making of this comic. Numerous zombies
from various time periods, however, definitely were.

**MIKE RICHARDSON** President and Publisher  **NEIL HANKERSON** Executive Vice President  **TOM WEDDLE** Chief Financial Officer  **RANDY STRADLEY** Vice President of Publishing  **MICHAEL MARTENS** Vice President of Book Trade Sales  **SCOTT ALLIE** Editor in Chief  **MATT PARKINSON** Vice President of Marketing  **DAVID SCROGGY** Vice President of Product Development  **DALE LaFOUNTAIN** Vice President of Information Technology  **DARLENE VOGEL** Senior Director of Print, Design, and Production  **KEN LIZZI** General Counsel  **DAVEY ESTRADA** Editorial Director  **CHRIS WARNER** Senior Books Editor  **DIANA SCHUTZ** Executive Editor  **CARY GRAZZINI** Director of Print and Development  **LIA RIBACCHI** Art Director  **CARA NIECE** Director of Scheduling  **MARK**

DONE! THE SUN VACUUM IS....DONE!

AAAH HA HA HA HA HA!

THAT'S BETTER.

HA HA

HA HA

HA HA

ZOMBIES, WE NEED TO *CELEBRATE* THIS DAY, FOR ONCE I *ACTIVATE* THIS MACHINE, IT WILL ABSORB ALL SUNLIGHT!

YOU! I DESIRE PARTY SNACKS!! TOAST ME SOME POP SMARTS... THE SCRUMPTIOUS BRAINY TREAT!

TAP
POP SMARTS TAP
TAP

AND THEN THE *PARTY* CAN BEGIN, FOR WHEN I *FLICK* THIS *SWITCH*...

OKAY. I CAN *DEAL* WITH THIS. I'LL FIND A SOLUTION.

WHAT ELSE IS A *GIANT* CRANIUM FOR?

BY MY CALCULATIONS, THIS EXPLOSION HAS NOT ONLY RIPPED MY SUN VACUUM *APART*, BUT...

...IT'S ALSO SENT *IRREPLACEABLE* PARTS *SKYROCKETING* ALL ACROSS THE ENTIRE PLANET, AND...

...EVEN THROUGH... *TIME ITSELF!*

BRAINS!

WHICH MEANS...*IT'S TIME* FOR ALL OF *YOU* TO PREPARE FOR A *TRIP!*

SO, USING THIS MACHINE, WE COULD *TRAVEL THROUGH TIME!*

WE COULD WITNESS SOME OF THE *GREATEST* EVENTS THAT MANKIND HAS EVER EXPERIENCED!

WE COULD WITNESS THE *AGE OF THE DINOSAURS!* MEET THE MOST IMPORTANT PEOPLE IN *ALL* OF HISTORY!

DISCOVER THE SECRETS OF THE AGES!

BLOBBLE PLOOB.

UNCLE DAVE SAYS, "WELL, YES. I SUPPOSE THERE'S *THAT.*"

BUT, MOSTLY HE'S HOPING TO GO BACK IN TIME AND FIND A TREASURED COPY OF *LEAPFROG QUARTERLY #5,* WHICH HAD ALL THE BEST TIPS ON PLAYING LEAPFROG.

SKRITCH SKRITCH

"IT'S THE *ONLY* ISSUE HE'S *MISSING.*"

LEAPFROG Quarterly #3

LEAPFROG Quarterly #4

GRA-GORGLE! FLING GRAK GRAK NARRRRRRRR.

HUH, WHAT'S CRAZY DAVE SAYING?

WHAT MY UNCLE DAVE SAID IS THAT THIS IS A MACHINE PART FROM A SUN VACUUM--A MACHINE THAT CAN ABSORB THE SUN'S RAYS.

THE TYPE OF MACHINE THAT ONLY DR. EDGAR ZOMBOSS WOULD BUILD.

BUT HE SAYS THERE'S AN AFTERTASTE THAT MEANS THE MACHINE HAS BEEN BLOWN UP, SOMEHOW, WITH ALL THE PARTS CATAPULTED THROUGHOUT TIME.

AND THESE SCRATCHES MEAN THAT ZOMBOSS HAS SENT HIS ZOMBIE MINIONS ALL THROUGHOUT TIME, SO THAT THEY CAN REBUILD THE MACHINE AND RULE THE WORLD.

CRAZY DAVE CAN...I MEAN, YOUR UNCLE DAVE CAN GET ALL OF THAT JUST FROM ONE CLUE?

YEP. ALSO...

$$24.1x = \frac{\Omega \, \text{IV}}{.0146}$$

4.13

...DR. ZOMBOSS PUTS TOO MUCH MACHINE OIL ON HIS SUN VACUUM, AND HIS FAVORITE FLAVOR OF POP SMARTS IS STRAWBERRY.

PTU!!

NATE! NATE!

OH! PULL OVER, GUYS. I KNOW THIS GIRL.

FREEZE

GET IN! I FOUND SOME AWESOME PLANTS!

I NAMED THIS ONE FRED, AND THIS ONE'S JEFF, AND THIS IS GRRAWRR-BEAR THE ULTIMATE FACE-PUNCHER.

WE HAVE PLANTS NOW! WE CAN FIGHT THESE ZOMBIES. NO PROBLEM!

ACTUALLY, THERE IS A PROBLEM.

PROBLEM?

PROBLEM.

BRAINS?

BRAINS.

SEE?

OH, YEAH. THAT ACTUALLY DOES QUALIFY AS A PROBLEM.

BRAINS?

BRAINS?

BRAINS?

POP SMARTS?

BRAINS?

NATE, ARE YOU OKAY? YOU DON'T LOOK SO GOOD.

YEAH. THAT'S BECAUSE YOU'RE SENSING MY FEAR.

BUT...

HUH. NOT SURE *HOW* IT HAPPENED, BUT I'VE BEEN CROWNED QUEEN OF EGYPT.

*NICE!*

BUT I'M *STRANDED* HERE UNTIL *NATE* AND *UNCLE DAVE* COME BACK WITH THE *TIME MACHINE.*

SO...WHAT TO DO...WHAT TO DO...

HMMM.

HEY! YOU ZOMBIE GUYS!

BUILD A *GIANT STATUE* OF ME ON TOP OF A HUGE *PYRAMID* THAT--

*ZORRRK!*

*SCREEECH!*

NEVER MIND! MY RIDE'S HERE!

OKAY, SO WE'RE BACK IN *TIME* IN THE AGE OF THE *DINOSAURS,* AND THAT *COULD* BE BAD.

BUT, IF WE MOVE VERY *QUIETLY,* AND WE *DON'T* ATTRACT A LOT OF ATTENTION, MAYBE WE CAN FIND THE *MACHINE PART* WITHOUT GETTING INTO ANY...

...TROUBLE.

*DINOSAURS!* SO... *AWESOME!*

CHECK IT OUT, PATRICE! *DINOSAURS!* PRETTY COOL, HUH?

UH, NATE. YOU KNOW THEY'RE *DANGEROUS,* RIGHT?

NAHHH... THEY'RE NOT *DANGEROUS!* THEY'RE *DINOSAURS!*

*SELFIE!*

CLICK

UH...OH...

WOW.

WELL, I GUESS EVERYTHING WAS BIGGER IN THE AGE OF DINOSAURS.

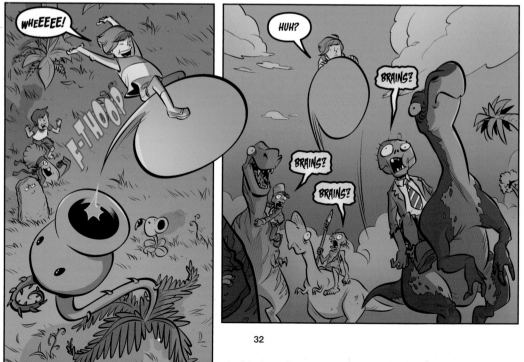

OH, NO! IT'S A WHOLE ZOMBIE VILLAGE!

Welcome to ZOMBIEVILLE

"COMPLETE WITH A GYMNASIUM!"

BRAINS?

BRAINS?

BRAINS?

BRAINS?

JUMP!

JUMP!

"AND A GROCERY STORE!"

PRESTON PENGUIN GROC

BRAINZ R OUT OF STOCK

OOOOH!

OOOH!

BRAINS!

LOOK, NATE! THEY MUST HAVE BEEN LIVING HERE FOR CENTURIES.

I SUPPOSE THAT MAKES SENSE. I MEAN, WITH A TIME MACHINE, THEY COULD HAVE BEEN SENT FARTHER BACK IN TIME THAN WE WENT.

THAT MEANS THEY'VE BEEN SEARCHING FOR THE LOST MACHINE PART FOR HUNDREDS OF YEARS--AND STILL HAVEN'T FOUND IT!

IT MUST BE HIDDEN REALLY WELL. HOW ARE WE GOING TO FIND IT?

WHY ISN'T CRAZY DAVE BRINGING US BACK THROUGH TIME?

BE *PATIENT*, NATE. IT SHOULD BE *ANY SECOND*.

IT'S *NOT LIKE* THE TIME MACHINE IS CURRENTLY *OUT OF OPERATION*, OWING TO HOW DAVE IS USING AN IMPORTANT PART OF IT...LIKE MAYBE THE *ROLLER SKATES*...TO PROP OPEN HIS WINDOW, SINCE IT WAS GETTING TOO WARM IN THE LAB, HUH?

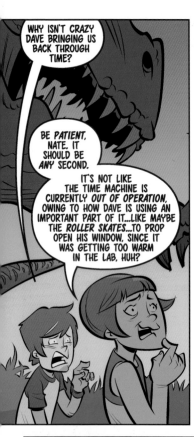

EANWHILE, MILLIONS OF YEARS IN THE FUTURE...

LA, LA, LA! GARBLE-GRABBLE LA!

OH, THAT'S *TOTALLY* HAPPENING.

OKAY, SO YOU AND I HAVE TO SURVIVE *LONG ENOUGH* FOR DAVE TO REMEMBER THAT HE SENT US BACK TO THE *AGE OF THE DINOSAURS* IN AN ATTEMPT TO *SAVE THE WORLD*.

YOU KNOW, THAT'S SOMETHING THAT *MOST OF US*, QUITE *FRANKLY*, WOULD *REMEMBER*.

WELL, WE NEED TO REMEMBER TO *FIGHT!*

*FIGHT?* I THOUGHT WE WERE GOING TO *RUN*.

EANWHILE...

*MUNCH MUNCH MUNCH*

WATCH IT-- ON THE RIGHT! NEANDERTHAL ZOMBIES!

EANWHILE...

WELCOME TO CHAPTER ONE OF ADVENTURES IN GARDENING.

PHINEAS JAMES THROTTLEBOTTOM STOOD LOOKING AT HIS GARDEN, ADMIRING THE RIPE TOMATOES, WHEN SUDDENLY A ZEPPELIN SOARED INTO VIEW!

LOOK OUT!

ZOMBIE DINOSAURS!

EANWHILE...

CHAPTER TWELVE...HERE THERE BE PEA-SHOOTERS!

PHINEAS LOOKED IN HORROR AT THE DISHEVELED FORM OF HIS SECRETARY, MISS PRIMPKINS. COULD IT BE THAT SHE WAS THE NEFARIOUS MADAME MOLE?

HERE ARE SOME ZOMBIES TO PUNCH! PLEASE BE PUNCHING THEM!

OOT?

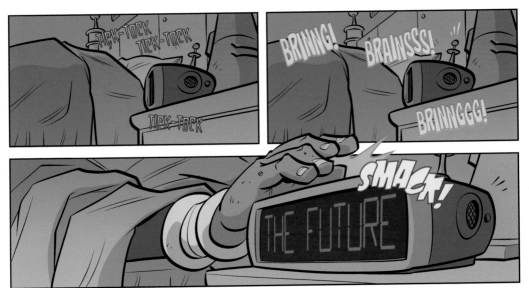

41

THEN LET'S PUT YOU TO THE TEST!

YOU DON'T GET BRAINS WITHOUT BEING TAUGHT, SO... HERE'S A LITTLE TEACHING!

FIRST LESSON! AN OBJECT IN MOTION TENDS TO STAY IN MOTION!

EXAMPLE A IS--MY FOOT!

MOTION!

STILL IN MOTION!

REMAINING IN MOTION!

END OF LESSON.

PATRICE?

PATRICE BLAZING IS SKILLED IN 452 TYPES OF COMBAT, INCLUDING GORILLA CHOP AND TOASTER FU!

NICE!

I'M WICKED AWESOME.

WHILE NATHANIEL TIMELY IS THE WORLD'S MOST SKILLED ANTI-ZOMBIE SCIENTIST.

HA! SEE?! I'M PRETTY COOL, TOO!

HE'S ALSO BEEN TAKING A LOT OF DANCE CLASSES, BECAUSE HE'S STILL EMBARRASSED ABOUT HOW POORLY HE DID AT THE DISCOTHEQUE IN 1979.

OH, YEAH. THAT WAS KIND OF EMBARRASSING...

IF YOU SEE EITHER OF THESE BRAIN-TOTING CRIMINALS, ALERT ME--DR. EDGAR ZOMBOSS--AT ONCE!

THEY ARE THE GREATEST THREAT OUR ZOMBIE DYNASTY HAS EVER KNOWN, AND SHOULD BE CONSIDERED EXTREMELY DANGEROUS.

UH-OH.

ZOMBIES!

WE NEED TO STOP THEM BEFORE THEY CAN ALERT DR. ZOMBOSS ABOUT--

ZOMBOSS ALERT BUTTON

NOT DURING NAPTIME, PLEASE

PUSH!

OOPS.

ZZZ

ZRRS

ZRAKK!

HMMM... MAYBE SHE'S RIGHT.

I'M A SCIENTIST NOW. I CAN HELP!

TOASTER FU!

WHAM

WHAM

WHAPPITY WHAM

LET'S SEE. *THIS* IS INTERESTING.

PLUTONIUM-BASED BROADCASTING SYSTEM WITH MAGNETIC PULSE WAVES.

FACE PUNCH!

IF I COULD WIRE IN ONE OF THESE E.M.PEACH PLANTS, I SHOULD BE ABLE TO *AMPLIFY* ITS SIGNAL.

THUMP

IT'S HERE! EYE ISLAND!

"THE ISLAND WHERE THE *DREAD PIRATE CHESTBEARD* BURIED HIS *TREASURE CHEST!*"

ARRR AND AYE! DIG DEEP, YE SCALAWAGS 'N' PIRATES!

YOU TOO, BIFFY!

"INCLUDING THE *MACHINE PART* ACCIDENTALLY SENT BACK FROM THE FUTURE. THE PART THAT *DR. ZOMBOSS* NEEDS IN ORDER TO COMPLETE HIS *SUN VACUUM MACHINE.*"

TOSS!

OOO! SHINY!

WE CAN'T LET ZOMBOSS GET TO THE PIECE *FIRST,* WHICH MEANS WE NEED TO *STEAL* IT FROM CHESTBEARD.

STEAL FROM A PIRATE?

YOU WANT US TO... STEAL...FROM... A...PIRATE?

THIS IS THE BEST THING EVER!

OKAY! LET'S GET THIS *FLOATING ISLAND* ON THE WAY, THEN!

EH?

**SHARK FIGHT!**

THAT WAS *AWESOME!* WE FOUGHT A *SHARK!* I'VE ALWAYS *WANTED* TO DO THAT!

YOU KNOW, YOU AND I SEEM TO HAVE *DIFFERENT* GOALS IN LIFE.

HUH? DON'T YOU WANT TO FIGHT ROBOTS? FIGHT *MONSTERS?* FIGHT *LIONS?* DEFEAT A HUGE PEPPERONI PIZZA?

THAT *LAST* ONE SOUNDS GOOD, BUT *FIRST* WE HAVE TO FIGHT ZOMBIES.

*SPEAKING* OF THAT, YOU GUYS *READY?* ONE, TWO, THREE...

"BECAUSE HIS MEN ARE A *TRAINED* GROUP OF *SKILLED* FIGHTERS. HARD TO BEAT. PLUS, THEY DON'T *SHOWER* VERY OFTEN. HARD TO *STOMACH*.

"AND OF COURSE WE NEED TO WORRY ABOUT THE *ZOMBIE NAVY*. THEY'RE *NOT* WELL TRAINED--OR ALL THAT *SMART*--BUT THERE'S SO *MANY* OF THEM THAT THEY BECOME DANGEROUS!"

...OTIS THE OARSMAN.

EH, I DID MY PART.

SMACK!

NOW THE TREASURE'S OURS!

HA HA HA HA HA!

WELL, IT WAS REALLY OURS TO *BEGIN WITH*, SINCE WE'RE THE ONES WHO BURIED IT HERE ON THE ISLAND.

GRANTED...BUT IT'S NOT TECHNICALLY TRUE THAT THE TREASURE WAS OURS TO BEGIN WITH. WE DID STEAL IT FROM OTHER PEOPLE.

OH, EXCELLENT POINT, BUBBLEPIPE PIRATE.

YES, YES, BUT MY POINT IS...

...NOBODY CAN TAKE IT AWAY FROM US!

BUT NEARBY...

WE HAVE TO TAKE IT AWAY FROM HIM!

AND UNFORTUNATELY...

THE TREASURE WILL BE MINE!

Meanwhile...

MEANWHILE...

FRED--THE PEASHOOTERS NEED POWER! JEFF--BLOW THAT GARGANTUAR BACK!

GRRAWRR-- I NEED YOU TO PUNCH ZOMBIES!

PUNCH SO MANY ZOMBIES!

THERE'S NO WAY TO STOP US! HA HA HA HA!

HA HA HA HA!

FWOOSH!

FWOOSH!

WHOOSH!

OKAY... I ADMIT THAT'S PROBLEMATIC...

BROB-GOBBLE FRENK JOBBLY-POOF!

OKAY, UNCLE DAVE SAYS HE HAS *ALL* THE PARTS TO THE SUN VACUUM! IF WE GIVE HIM SOME *TIME*, HE CAN CHANGE IT AROUND...

"...SO THAT INSTEAD OF *DRAINING* THE SUN'S POWER, *VACUUMING* IT UP THE WAY ZOMBOSS *INTENDED* THE MACHINE TO BE USED..."

YES! YES!

"...WE CAN USE IT TO *MAGNIFY* THE SUN'S RAYS...GIVING THE PLANTS EVEN *MORE* POWER."

NO! NO! NO!

BUT...*WHILE* DAVE IS FINISHING HIS WORK ON THE MACHINE, HE WONDERS IF WE COULD DO HIM A FEW *FAVORS.*

SURE! WHAT'S HE NEED?

OKAY...FIRST HE NEEDS THE TOE-MASSAGING SHOES HE INVENTED, AND WE HAVE TO MOVE THE TELEVISION IN HERE SO THAT HE CAN WATCH HIS *PANDORA'S PLANTS* SOAP OPERA...

...AND HE'D LIKE SOME LEMONADE WITH ICE CUBES IN THE SHAPE OF BUNNIES... AND TWO FISHING POLES, HIS ROLLER SKATES...

...A SUNFLOWER THAT CAN PLAY THE DRUMS, AND...

...IN ORDER TO GIVE HIM *TIME* TO *FINISH* THE WORK, HE'D *REALLY* APPRECIATE IT...

AND SO...

HERE! USE THIS TO SPRAY *TIME PARTICLES* AT THE ZOMBIES. THEY'LL BE CAUGHT IN A *TIME LOOP.*

BRAINS!

BRAINS!

BRAINS!

AARGH!

HA! THEY JUST KEEP REPEATING!

BRAINS!

NOW UNCLE DAVE CAN WORK ON THE SUN MACHINE ALL HE WANTS.

BRAINS!

AARGH!

WE HAVE PLENTY OF TIME.

RIGHT. BUT *NOW* I'M WONDERING...

DO WE HAVE PLENTY OF *LEMONADE?*

BRAINS!

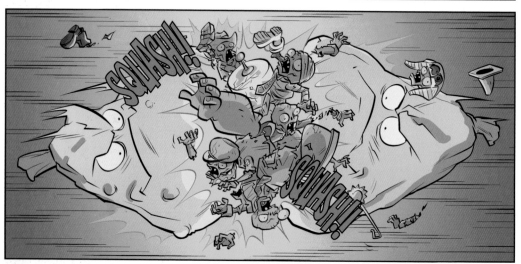

AND THEN...

FLEMBARG GRATTLE!

WELL, THAT'S *THAT*. WE'LL *NEVER* HAVE TO DEAL WITH *HIM* AGAIN.

ZOMBIE REMOVAL SERVICE

Specializing in imprisoning Zomboos until he inevitably escapes again

AND OF COURSE...

...A PIZZA PARTY!

HELLO, PIRATE PIZZA? WE'D LIKE TWELVE LARGE PIZZAS, PLEASE. FIVE WITH PEPPERONI AND POMEGRANATES, AND SEVEN WITH *BIG CHUNKS OF SUNSHINE!*

DING DONG!

PIZZA'S HERE!

HUH? CHESTBEARD?

AYE AND ARRRR. DONE GOT ME *LOST IN TIME*, I DID.

OH, I FEEL KIND OF *BAD* ABOUT THAT.

WHY DON'T YOU COME IN AND HAVE SOME PIZZA WITH US?

ARRR. AND AYE!

TREASURE!

THE END!

Paul Tobin

Ron Chan

Matthew J. Rainwater

# CREATOR BIOS

**PAUL TOBIN** is a critically acclaimed bald guy who had his first encounter with zombies when he watched the 1973 film *Children Shouldn't Play with Dead Things* on late-night television during one of the first times his parents ever left him alone. They returned to find him cowering in the kitchen with a knife. Paul eventually recovered enough mental stability to go on to write hundreds of comics for Marvel, DC, Dark Horse, and many others, including creator-owned titles such as *Colder* and *Bandette*, as well as *Prepare to Die!*—his debut novel. Paul's favorite zombie-fighting plants are the Cattail, the Snow Pea, and the Spikerock.

**RON CHAN** is a cartoonist, storyboard artist, and illustrator born and raised in Portland, Oregon. He graduated from the Savannah College of Art and Design in 2005, and is now a member of the Portland-based art collective Periscope Studio. His comic-book work has been published by Dark Horse, Marvel, and Image Comics, and storyboarding work of his includes boards for 3-D animation, gaming, internal development, user-experience design, and advertising for clients such as Microsoft, Amazon Kindle, Nike, and Sega. He really likes drawing the Bonk Choy.

Residing in the cool, damp forests of Portland, Oregon, **MATTHEW J. RAINWATER** is a freelance illustrator whose work has been featured in advertising, web design, and independent video games. On top of this, he also self-publishes several comic books, including *Garage Raja* and *Trailer Park Warlock*, both of which can be found at MattJRainwater .com. Matt is knee deep into *Plants vs. Zombies 2* but has yet to venture into the Far Future and Dark Ages worlds. His favorite zombie-bashing strategy utilizes a line of Bonk Choy with a Wall-nut front guard and Threepeater covering fire.

# MORE DARK HORSE ALL-AGES TITLES

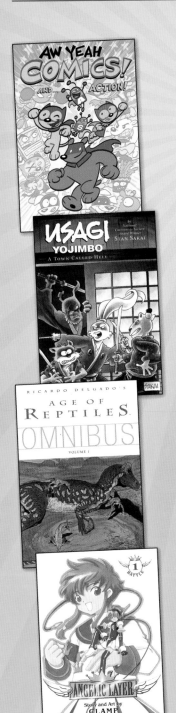

## AW YEAH COMICS! AND . . . ACTION!

Cornelius and Alowicious are just your average comic book store employees, but when trouble strikes, they are . . . Action Cat and Adventure Bug! Join their epic all-ages adventures as they face off—with the help of Adorable Cat and Shelly Bug—against their archnemesis, Evil Cat, and his fiendish friends!

ISBN 978-1-61655-558-0 | $12.99

## USAGI YOJIMBO

In his latest adventure, the rabbit *ronin* Usagi finds himself caught between competing gang lords fighting for control of a town called Hell, confronting a *nukekubi*—a flying cannibal head—and crossing paths with the demon Jei!

*Volume 25: Fox Hunt*
ISBN 978-1-59582-726-5 | $16.99

*Volume 26: Traitors of the Earth* | $16.99
ISBN 978-1-59582-910-8

*Volume 27: A Town Called Hell* | $16.99
ISBN 978-1-59582-970-2

## AGE OF REPTILES OMNIBUS

When Ricardo Delgado first set his sights on creating comics, he crafted an epic tale about the most unlikely cast of characters: dinosaurs. Since that first Eisner-winning foray into the world of sequential art he has returned to his critically acclaimed *Age of Reptiles* again and again, each time crafting a captivating saga about his saurian subjects.

ISBN 978-1-59582-683-1 | $24.99

## ANGELIC LAYER BOOK 1

Junior-high student Misaki Suzuhara just arrived in Tokyo to live with her TV-star aunt and attend the prestigious Eriol Academy. But what excites Misaki most is Angelic Layer—an arena game where you control a miniature robot fighter with your mind! Can Misaki's enthusiasm and skill take her to the top of the arena?

ISBN 978-1-61655-021-9 | $19.99